D1266390

FLITZY BOOKS .COM™

Where love and imagination flit, flutter, and fly!

Copyright © 2014 Eve Coberly
Special thank you to Joy Bean, text editor.

Printed in the United States of America

Print Edition 2014

For more books, activities, and videos visit:

http://www.flitzybooks.com

Dedicated to the reader...

that you **enjoy** a cup of **warm chocolate** with the people you **love**.

"Alright class," **Mrs. Peacock** said, "let's talk about **holiday** treats."
"Tell me your favorite **winter** goodie-the one you **LOVE** to eat."

Sally Jones **squirmed** in her seat and **yelled**,
"I LOVE gingerbread!"

Then **Michael Smith** said in a soft whisper,
"I like fruitcake instead."

Next Sydney Clark **screamed** from the back,

"A soufflé with lemon zest!"

Then Wyatt McFinn said with a **BIG** grin,

"Cherry pie is the VERY best!"

"Can I go next?" Marvin Peters asked, waving his hand up high.

"Alright Marvin," Mrs. Peacock said, "tell us what you like to try."

Marvin stood **tall** by his desk holding a large **stack** of papers.
He was ready to share his **sweet** treat-the one that he **most** favors.

My Favorite Winter Treat
by Marvin Peters
December 18th, 2016

There is something that I really love, that tastes so very DREAMY.

I've changed **its** name to **WARM** 'cause it's **best** when it's **not** **TOO** **HOT**.

CHOCOLATE MATH

TOO **HOT** + CHOCOLATE = ☹

WARM + CHOCOLATE = ☺

Here are a few examples of how WARM chocolate hits the SPOT.

WARM chocolate helps me **cheer** for my favorite **hockey** team.

TOO **HOT** turns my chants into loud and painful **screams.**

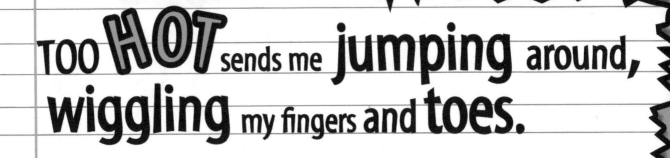

TOO **HOT** sends me **jumping** around, **wiggling** my fingers and **toes.**

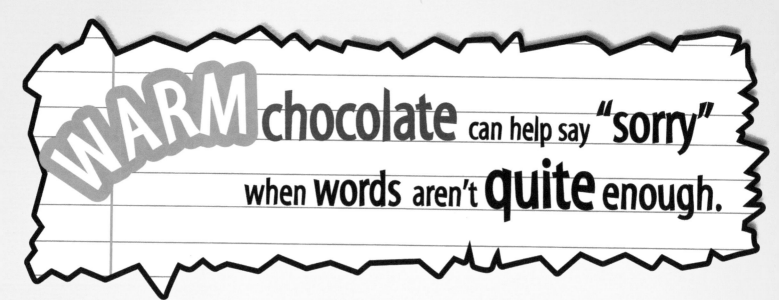

What I love **most** about WARM

can be **summed** up **here** at the **very** end:

#1 Reason

About the good things in your life, that make it so very sweet. Like your mom's light bedtime kiss, and your dad's TOP SECRET treat.

Hi! My name is Eve and I am the author and creator of Warm Chocolate. One of the things I like to do when I create picture books is use both drawings and real life photos. I challenge you to go back through the pages and see if you can find what is real in my illustrations. When you think you've found them all, turn the next page to see if you were right.

My daughter's winter coat and half of our family couch (I cut and pasted two ends of the couch together)

Our house in Daegu, South Korea

Picture I took of my husband and son as they approach Lake Erie at sunset Summer, 2014

Our house at Fort Leavenworth, Kansas

Delicious marshmallow

Mug (says New Orleans on the other side)

German school desk and chair we got while living in Germany from 2001-2005

Paper airplane made by my husband

WARM CHOCOLATE RECIPE

Ingredients:

2 tablespoons unsweetened cocoa powder

Pinch of salt

Pinch of cinnamon (optional)

1 cup milk

1/4 teaspoon of vanilla extract

11/2 tablespoons sugar (add more if you want it sweeter)

marshmallows (optional)

DIRECTIONS:

With adult supervision mix together all ingredients in a small sauce pan. Cook over medium heat and stir until hot. Remove from heat and let it sit until it's at a nice WARM temperature. Top with marshmallows and enjoy with the people you love.